Non-Verbal Reasoning

The 11+ Practice Book

with Assessment Tests

For the CEM (Durham University) test

Ages
7-8

Practise • Prepare • Pass

Everything your child needs for 11+ success

How to use this Practice Book

This book is divided into three parts — Spotting Patterns, 3D Shapes and Assessment Tests. There are answers and detailed explanations in the pull-out section at the back of the book.

Spotting Patterns

- Each section contains practice questions focusing on one of the main concepts your child will need to understand for the Non-Verbal Reasoning part of the test.

- These pages can help your child build up the different skills they'll need for the real test.

3D Shapes

- This part concentrates on the skills your child will need to tackle the 3D shape questions in the test.

Assessment Tests

- The third part of the book contains eleven assessment tests, each with a mix of question types.

- You can print off multiple-choice answer sheets from our website, www.cgplearning.co.uk/11+, so your child can practise taking the tests as if they're sitting the real thing.

- If you want to give your child timed practice, set a time limit of 15 minutes for each test.

- The tests get harder from 1 to 11, so don't be surprised if your child finds the later ones more tricky.

- Talk your child through the answers to the questions they got wrong. This will help them understand questions that work in a similar way when they come up against them in later tests.

- Your child should aim for a mark of around 85% (20 questions correct) in each test. If they score less than this, use their results to work out the areas they need more practice on.

- If they haven't managed to finish the test in time, they need to work on increasing their speed, whereas if they have made a lot of mistakes, they need to work more carefully.

- Keep track of your child's scores using the progress chart on the inside back cover of the book.

Published by CGP

Editors:
Ceara Hayden, Gordon Henderson, Sharon Keeley-Holden, Rachel Kordan, Kirstie McHale, Anthony Muller, Rebecca Tate and Ben Train.

With thanks to Glenn Rogers and Judy Hornigold for the proofreading.

Please note that CGP is not associated with CEM or The University of Durham in any way. This book does not include any official questions and it is not endorsed by CEM or The University of Durham.

CEM, Centre for Evaluation and Monitoring, Durham University and *The University of Durham* are all trademarks of The University of Durham.

ISBN: 978 1 84762 569 4

Printed by Elanders Ltd, Newcastle upon Tyne
Clipart from Corel®

Based on the classic CGP style created by Richard Parsons.

CONTENTS

Shapes

Most questions will have shapes in them like circles, squares or triangles.

1. How many **sides** does each shape have?

a.   b.   c.   d.   e. 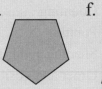   f.

<u>6</u>   __   __   __   __   __

2. How many figures have the **same shape** head as the figure inside the square?

Number of heads that are the **same shape**: ____

Find the Figure Like the First Two

Work out which option is most like the two figures on the left.

Example:

        |

    a   b   c   d

All figures must have three sides. (<u>b</u>)

3. |

    a   b   c   d

(____)

4. |

    a   b   c   d

(____)

5.

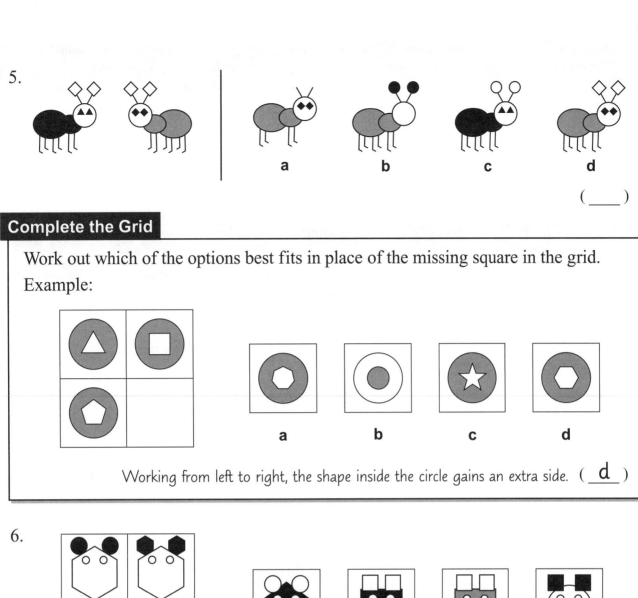

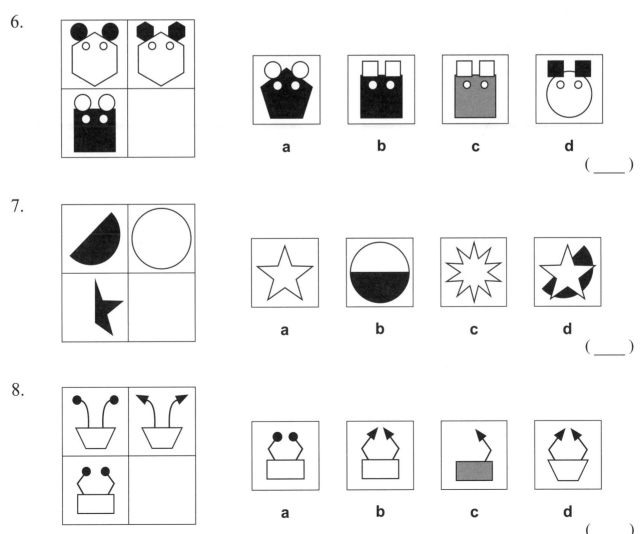

Counting

Counting things can help you find the answer to lots of questions.

1. How many **stars** are there in each square?

a.   b.   c.   d.   e.   f.

_3_   __   __   __   __   __

2. How many bees have the **same number** of **stripes** as the bee inside the square?

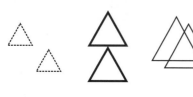

Number of bees with the **same number** of **stripes**: ____

Find the Figure Like the First Three

Work out which option is the most like the three figures on the left.

Example:

         a   b   c   d

Each figure must have two triangles. (_a_)

3.

         a   b   c   d

(___)

4.

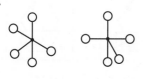

         a   b   c   d

(___)

5.

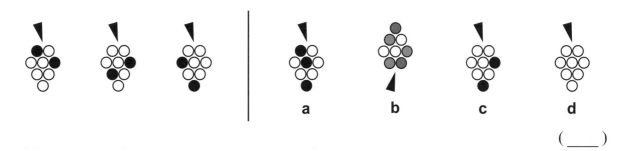

(___)

Complete the Series

Work out which of the options best fits in place of the missing square in the series.
Example:

                          a   b   c   d

A new, smaller hexagon is added to the middle of the figure in each series square. (_a_)

6.

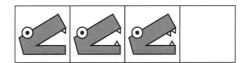

(___)

7.

(___)

8.

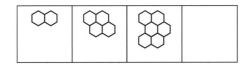

(___)

Spotting Patterns

Pointing

Things like arrows and triangles can point in different directions.

Warm Up

1. How many arrows are **pointing away** from the circle in each figure?

   a.   b.   c.   d.   e.   f.

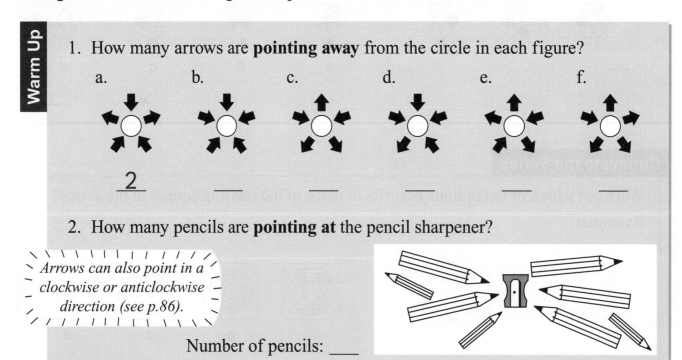

   <u>2</u>   ___   ___   ___   ___   ___

2. How many pencils are **pointing at** the pencil sharpener?

Arrows can also point in a clockwise or anticlockwise direction (see p.86).

Number of pencils: ___

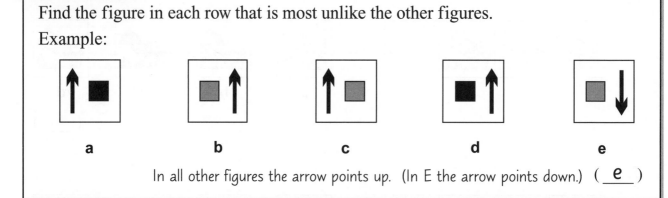

Odd One Out

Find the figure in each row that is most unlike the other figures.

Example:

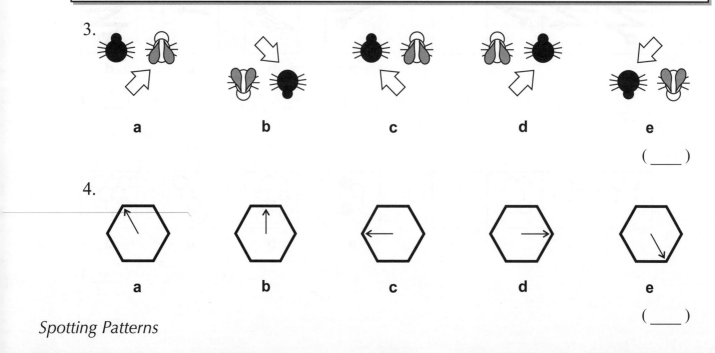

   a   b   c   d   e

In all other figures the arrow points up. (In E the arrow points down.) (*e*)

3.

a   b   c   d   e

(___)

4.

a   b   c   d   e

(___)

5.

a   b   c   d   e

(___)

Find the Figure Like the First Two

Work out which option is most like the two figures on the left.

Example:

  |

                                         a   b   c   d

In all figures the arrow must point at the black corner of a triangle. (_a_)

6.

 |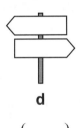

                                         a   b   c   d

(___)

7.

  |

                                         a   b   c   d

(___)

8.

  |

                                         a   b   c   d

(___)

Spotting Patterns

Shading and Line Types

Look out for shapes with different shadings, as well as lines that are dotted or dashed.

Warm Up

1. How many **black shapes** are there in each figure?

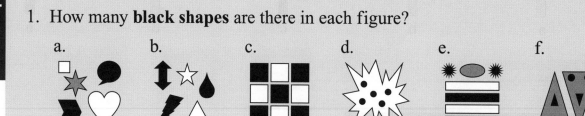

a.   b.   c.   d.   e.   f.

<u> 2 </u>   ___   ___   ___   ___   ___

2. How many shirts have the **same kind** of **stripes** as the shirt inside the square?

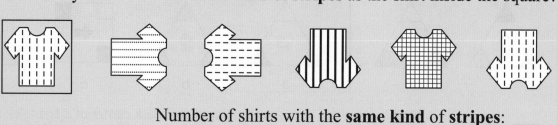

Number of shirts with the **same kind** of **stripes**: ____

Odd One Out

Find the figure in each row that is most unlike the other figures.

Example:

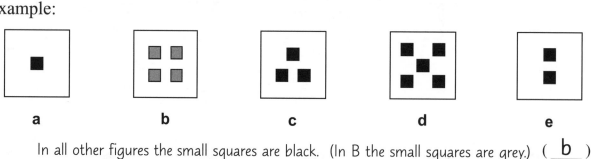

a   b   c   d   e

In all other figures the small squares are black. (In B the small squares are grey.) (<u>b</u>)

3.

   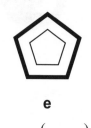

a   b   c   d   e

(___)

4.

a   b   c   d   e

Spotting Patterns

(___)

5.

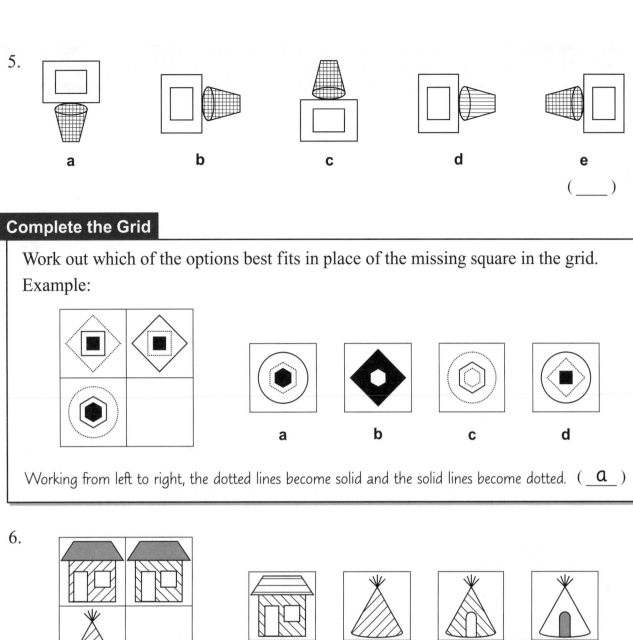

a   b   c   d   e

(___)

Complete the Grid

Work out which of the options best fits in place of the missing square in the grid.

Example:

a   b   c   d

Working from left to right, the dotted lines become solid and the solid lines become dotted. (_a_)

6.

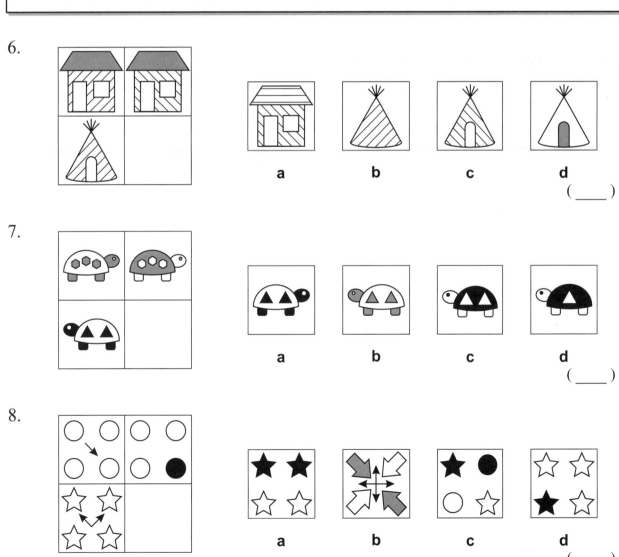

a   b   c   d

(___)

7.

a   b   c   d

(___)

8.

a   b   c   d

(___)

Spotting Patterns

Order and Position

In some questions shapes move around or change order.

1. Where is the star inside the square? Write **top**, **bottom**, **left** or **right**.

a.   b.   c.   d.   e.   f.

_____top_____   _____   _____   _____   _____   _____

2. Start at the star and move round the circle in a clockwise direction. How many figures have the small shapes in the **same order** as the figure inside the square?

Number of figures with the **same order** of small shapes: ____

Find the Figure Like the First Three

Work out which option is most like the three figures on the left.

Example:

     |

a   b   c   d

All figures must have one black dot inside the large white shape at the bottom. (_b_)

3.

     |

a   b   c   d

(____)

4.

   |

a   b   c   d

(____)

5.

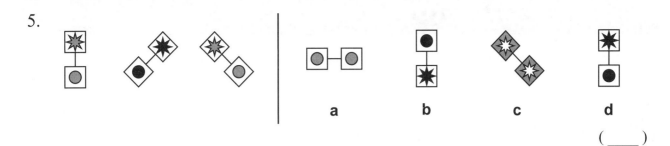

a   b   c   d

(___)

Complete the Pair

Look at how the first figure is changed, and then work out which option would look like the third figure if you changed it in the same way.

Example:

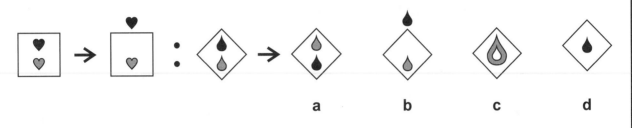

a   b   c   d

The small black shape moves up so that it is above the white shape. (__b__)

6.

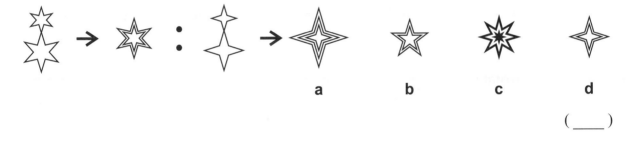

a   b   c   d

(___)

7.

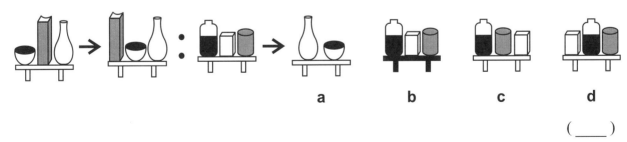

a   b   c   d

(___)

8.

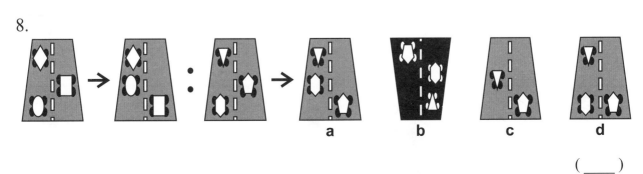

a   b   c   d

(___)

Spotting Patterns

Rotation

Rotation is when a shape is turned in a clockwise or anticlockwise direction.

Warm Up

1. Work out whether the black shape is a **90 degree rotation** of the white shape.
   Write **yes** if it is and **no** if it isn't.

 a.   b.   c.   d.   e.   f.

___yes___   _____   _____   _____   _____   _____

2. How many figures are **identical** to the left-hand figure apart
   from being **rotated differently**?

See p.86 for more about rotation.

Number of **identical figures**: ____

Rotate the Figure

Work out which option would look like the figure on the left if it was rotated.

Example:

 Rotate

a   b   c   d

The figure rotates 90 degrees clockwise. (__a__)

3.

 Rotate

a   b   c   d

(____)

4.

 Rotate

a   b   c   d

(____)

Spotting Patterns

5.

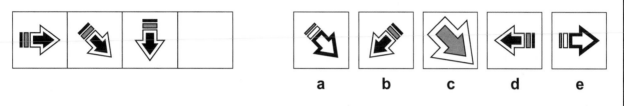

a   b   c   d

(____)

Complete the Series

Work out which of the options best fits in place of the missing square in the series.

Example:

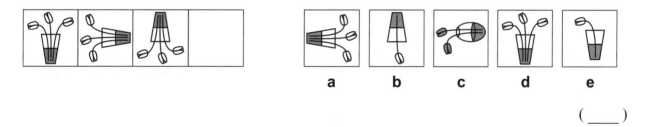

a   b   c   d   e

The arrow rotates 45 degrees clockwise in each series square. (_b_)

6.

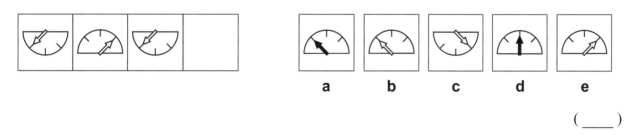

a   b   c   d   e

(____)

7.

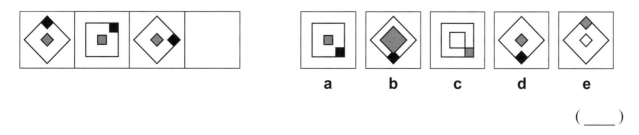

a   b   c   d   e

(____)

8.

a   b   c   d   e

(____)

Spotting Patterns

Reflection

A reflection of a shape is how it would look if it was put next to a mirror.

Warm Up

1. Work out whether the first figure has been **reflected** across the dotted line to make the second. Write **yes** if it has been reflected and **no** if it has not.

a.   b.   c.   d.   e.   f.

__yes__ _____ _____ _____ _____ _____

2. How many of the hats below are **reflections** of the hat in the square? The reflections might be **rotated**.

Number of **reflected hats**: ____

Reflect the Figure

Work out which option would look like the figure on the left if it was reflected over the line.

Example:

Reflect

a b c d

A and C have the wrong shading. B has the wrong shapes. (_d_)

Reflect

3.

a b c d

(____)

Reflect

4.

a b c d

(____)

Spotting Patterns

5.

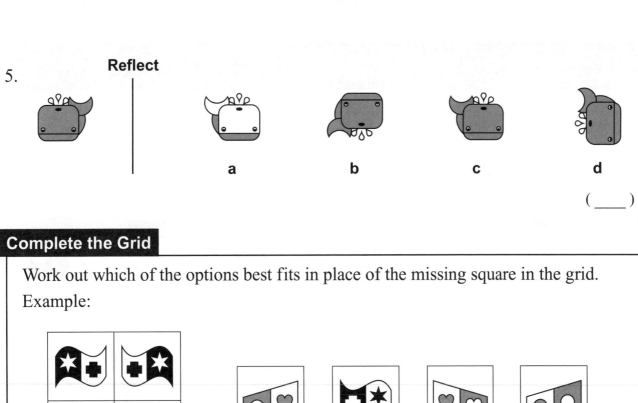

Reflect

a   b   c   d

(____)

Complete the Grid

Work out which of the options best fits in place of the missing square in the grid.

Example:

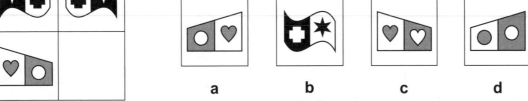

a   b   c   d

Working from left to right, the figure reflects across. (_a_)

6.

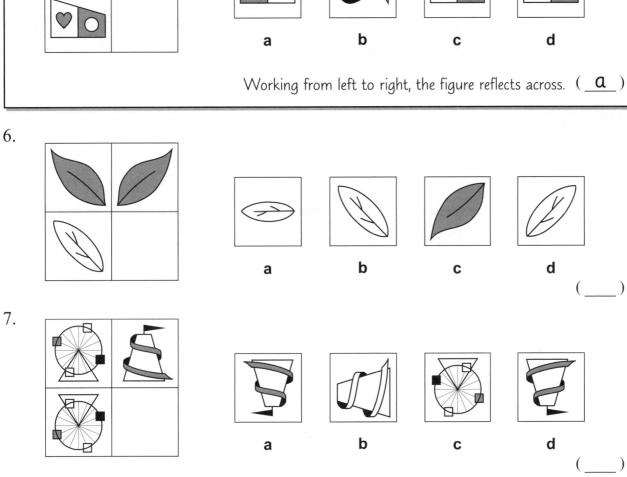

a   b   c   d

(____)

7.

a   b   c   d

(____)

8.

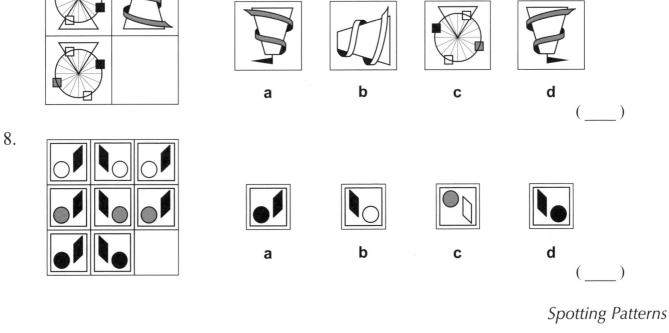

a   b   c   d

(____)

Layering

Shapes can be on top of, or underneath, other shapes.

1. Which shape is **at the front** of these figures?

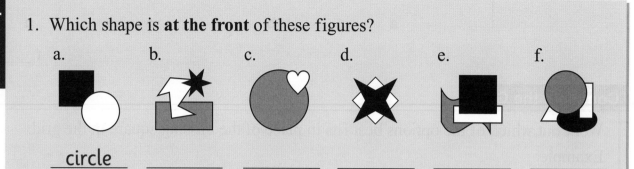

a.   b.   c.   d.   e.   f.

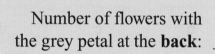

<u>circle</u>   _____   _____   _____   _____   _____

2. How **many** of these flowers have the grey petal at the **back**?

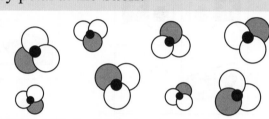

Number of flowers with
the grey petal at the **back**: ____

Odd One Out

Find the figure in each row that is most unlike the other figures.
Example:

a   b   c   d   e

In all other figures, the white circle is at the front. (In A it's behind the square.) (_a_)

3.

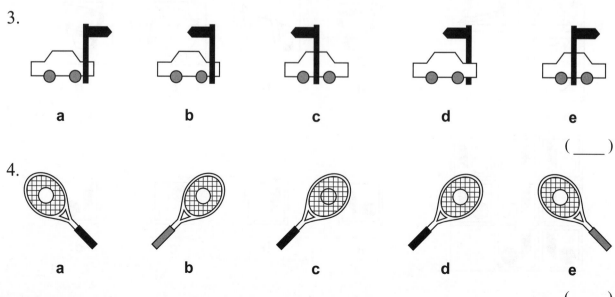

a   b   c   d   e

(____)

4.

a   b   c   d   e

(____)

Spotting Patterns

5.

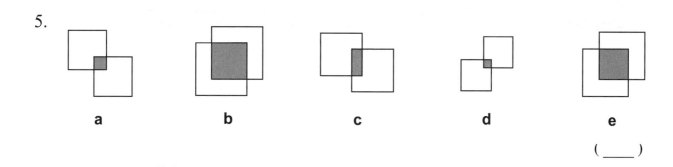

| a | b | c | d | e |

(___)

Complete the Pair

Look at how the first figure is changed, and then work out which option
would look like the third figure if you changed it in the same way.
Example:

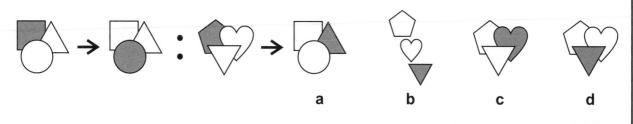

The grey shading moves from the back shape to the front shape. (**d**)

6.

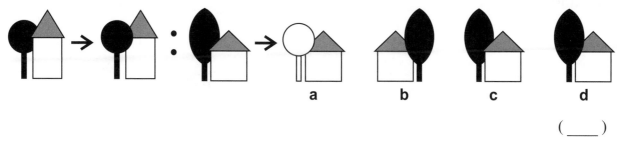

(___)

7.

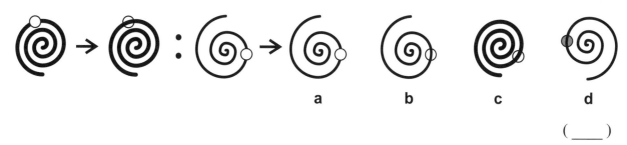

(___)

8.

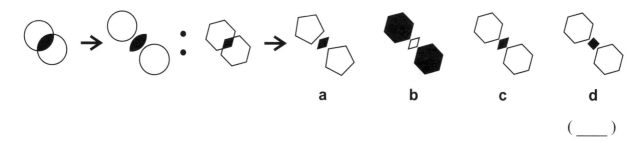

(___)

Spotting Patterns

3D Shapes

You might need to imagine what a 3D shape would look like from different angles.

1. If you looked at each figure from above, how many blocks could you see?

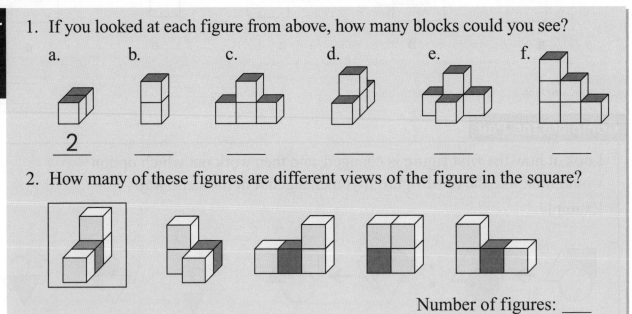

   a.   b.   c.   d.   e.   f.

   <u>2</u>   ___   ___   ___   ___   ___

2. How many of these figures are different views of the figure in the square?

                                        Number of figures: ___

Look at the Figure from the Top

Look at the figure on the left. What would it look like if you saw it from the top?
Choose the option on the right which looks like this.

Example:

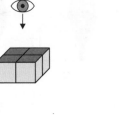   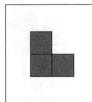   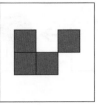

              a   b   c   d

Four blocks are visible from the top and they make a square. (**b**)

3.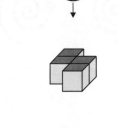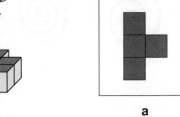

              a   b   c   d   (___)

4.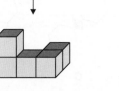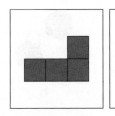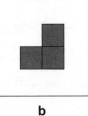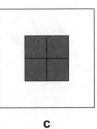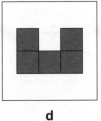

              a   b   c   d   (___)

5.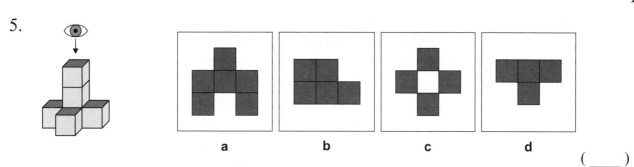

(___)

Look at the Figure from the Right

Look at the figure on the left. What would it look like if you saw it from the right-hand side? Choose the option on the right which looks like this.

Example:

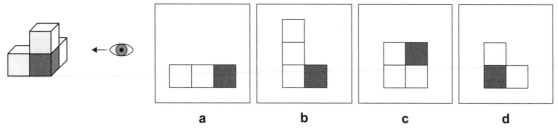

Three blocks are visible from the right. There should be two blocks at the bottom. (__d__)

6.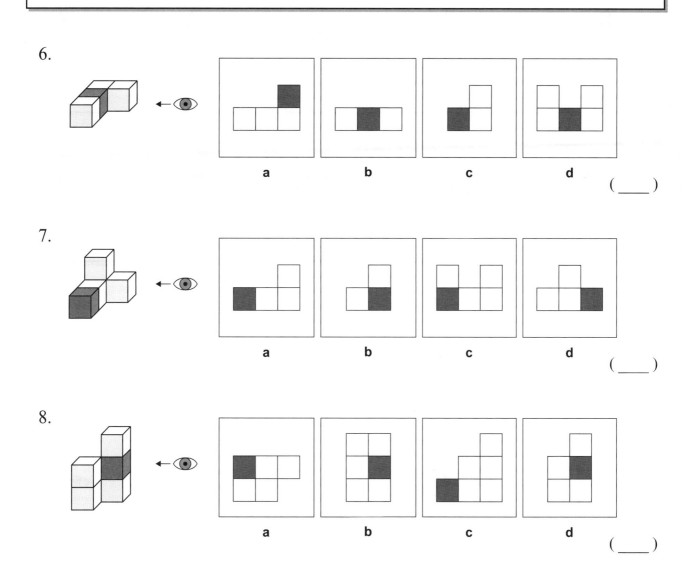

(___)

7.

(___)

8.

(___)

Assessment Test 1

You can print **multiple-choice answer sheets** for these questions from our website — go to www.cgplearning.co.uk/11+. If you'd prefer to answer them in standard write-in format, just circle the letter underneath your answer. The test should take around 15 minutes.

Section 1 — Reflect the Figure

Work out which option would look like the figure on the left if it was reflected over the line.

Example:

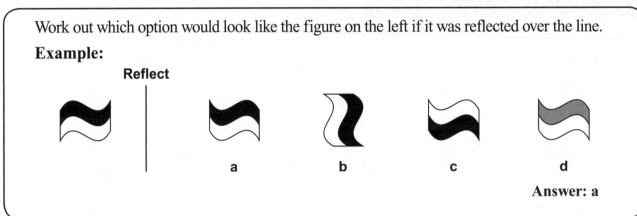

Answer: **a**

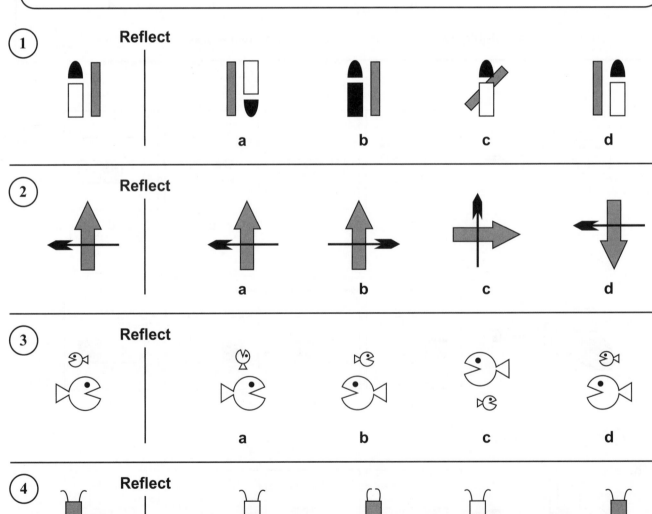

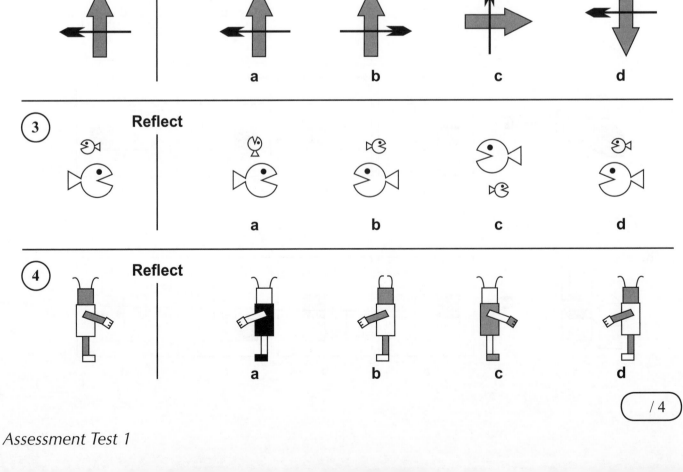

/ 4

Section 2 — Complete the Pair

Look at how the first figure is changed, and then work out which option would look like the third figure if you changed it in the same way.

Example:

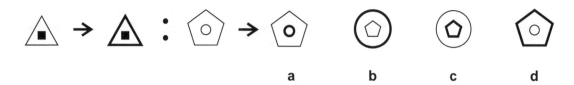

Answer: d

---

(1)

 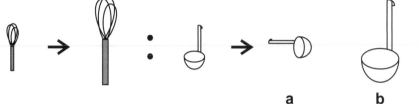 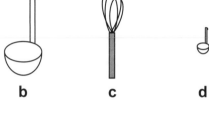

                                             a   b   c   d

---

(2)

                                             a   b   c   d

---

(3)

                                             a   b   c   d

---

(4)

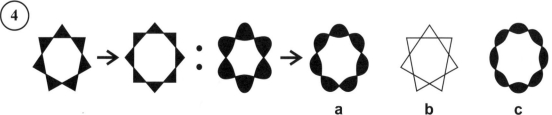 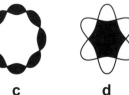

                                             a   b   c   d

/ 4

Assessment Test 1

Section 3 — Odd One Out

Find the figure in each row that is most unlike the other figures.

Example:

a   b   c   d   e

Answer: a

(1)

a   b   c   d   e

(2)

_ _ _ _ _   _ _ _ _   _ _ _   __ __   _ _ _ _ _ _

a   b   c   d   e

(3)

a   b   c   d   e

(4)

a   b   c   d   e

/ 4

Section 4 — Complete the Grid

Work out which of the options best fits in place of the missing square in the grid.

Example:

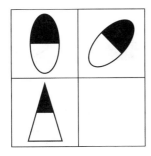

a   b   c   d

Answer: b

1

a   b   c   d

2

a   b   c   d

3

a   b   c   d

4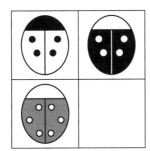

a   b   c   d

/ 4

Assessment Test 1

Section 5 — Find the Figure Like the First Two

Work out which option is most like the two figures on the left.

Example:

a   b   c   d

Answer: a

1

a   b   c   d

2

a   b   c   d

3

a   b   c   d

4

a   b   c   d

/ 4

Section 6 — Complete the Series

Work out which of the options best fits in place of the missing square in the series.

Example:

                                       a   **b**   **c**   **d**

Answer: d

1

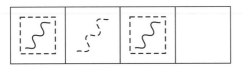

                                       a   **b**   **c**   **d**

2

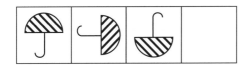

                                       a   **b**   **c**   **d**

3

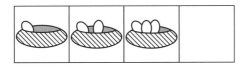

                                       a   **b**   **c**   **d**

4

                                       a   **b**   **c**   **d**

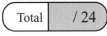

END OF TEST

Assessment Test 2

You can print **multiple-choice answer sheets** for these questions from our website — go to
www.cgplearning.co.uk/11+. If you'd prefer to answer them in standard write-in format,
just circle the letter underneath your answer. The test should take around 15 minutes.

Section 1 — Complete the Pair

Look at how the first figure is changed, and then work out which option would look
like the third figure if you changed it in the same way.

Example:

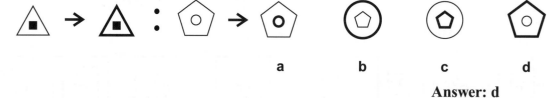

Answer: d

(1)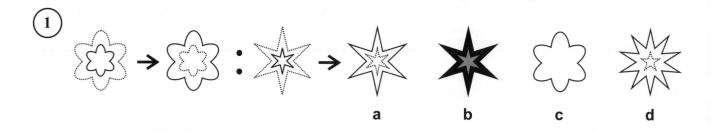

(2)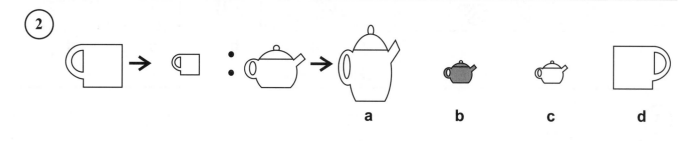

(3)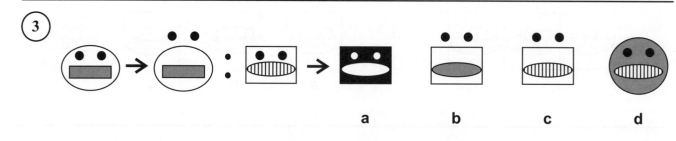

(4)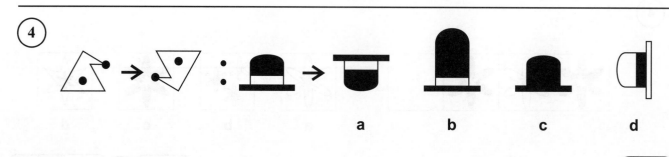

/ 4

Section 2 — Rotate the Figure

Work out which option would look like the figure on the left if it was rotated.

Example:

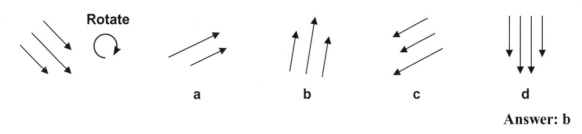

a   b   c   d

Answer: b

(1)

  Rotate

a   b   c   d

(2)

  Rotate

a   b   c   d

(3)

 Rotate

a   b   c   d

(4)

 Rotate

a   b   c   d

/ 4

Assessment Test 2

Section 3 — Complete the Series

Work out which of the options best fits in place of the missing square in the series.

Example:

  a   b   c   d

Answer: d

(1)

  a   b   c   d

(2)

  a   b   c   d

(3)

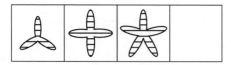

  a   b   c   d

(4)

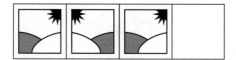

  a   b   c   d

/ 4

Section 4 — Odd One Out

Find the figure in each row that is most unlike the other figures.

Example:

a   b   c   d

Answer: a

1

a   b   c   d

2

a   b   c   d

3

a   b   c   d

4

a   b   c   d

/ 4

Assessment Test 2

Section 5 — Complete the Grid

Work out which of the options best fits in place of the missing square in the grid.

Example:

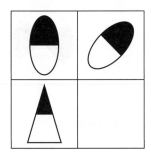

a   b   c   d

Answer: b

 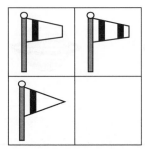 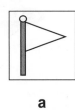 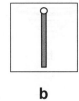

a   b   c   d

a   b   c   d

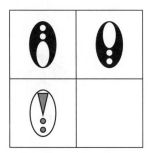

a   b   c   d

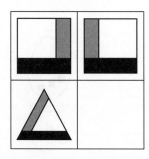 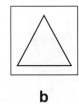 

a   b   c   d

/ 4

Section 6 — Find the Figure Like the First Three

Work out which option is the most like the three figures on the left.

Example:

   |

                                         a   b   c   d

Answer: b

1 |

                                         a   b   c   d

2 |

                                         a   b   c   d

3 |

                                         a   b   c   d

4 |

                                         a   b   c   d

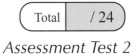

/ 4   Total   / 24

END OF TEST   *Assessment Test 2*

Assessment Test 3

You can print **multiple-choice answer sheets** for these questions from our website — go to www.cgplearning.co.uk/11+. If you'd prefer to answer them in standard write-in format, just circle the letter underneath your answer. The test should take around 15 minutes.

Section 1 — Odd One Out

Find the figure in each row that is most unlike the other figures.

Example:

    a   b   c   d   e

Answer: a

1

    a   b   c   d   e

2

    a   b   c   d   e

3

    a   b   c   d   e

4

    a   b   c   d   e

/ 4

Section 2 — Find the Figure Like the First Two

Work out which option is most like the two figures on the left.

Example:

a   b   c   d

Answer: a

---

1 

                            a   b   c   d

2

                            a   b   c   d

3

                            a   b   c   d

---

4   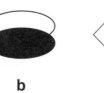

                            a   b   c   d

/ 4

Assessment Test 3

Section 3 – Reflect the Figure

Work out which option would look like the figure on the left if it was reflected over the line.

Example:

Reflect

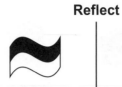

a   b   c   d

Answer: a

---

 1   **Reflect**

a   b   c   d

---

2   **Reflect**

a   b   c   d

---

3   **Reflect**

a   b   c   d

---

4   **Reflect**

a   b   c   d

/ 4

Section 4 — Complete the Grid

Work out which of the options best fits in place of the missing square in the grid.

Example:

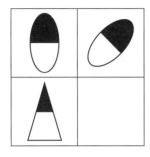

a

b

c

d

Answer: b

1

a

b

c

d

2

a

b

c

d

3
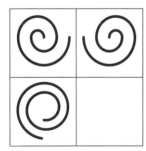

a

b

c

d

4

a

b

c

d

/ 4

Section 5 — Look at the Figure from the Top

Look at the figure on the left. What would it look like if you saw it from the top? Choose the option on the right which looks like this.

Example:

a b c d

Answer: b

1

a b c d

2

a b c d

3

a b c d

4

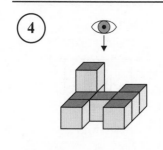 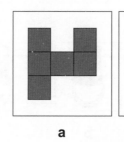 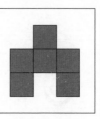 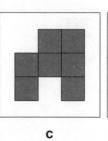 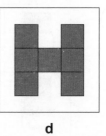

a b c d

/ 4

Section 6 — Rotate the Figure

Work out which option would look like the figure on the left if it was rotated.

Example:

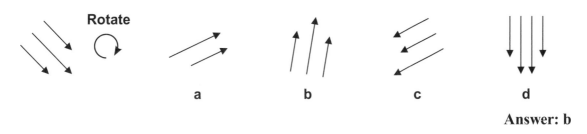

a   b   c   d

Answer: b

a   b   c   d

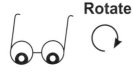

a   b   c   d

a   b   c   d

a   b   c   d

/ 4   Total / 24

END OF TEST

Assessment Test 3

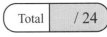

Assessment Test 4

You can print **multiple-choice answer sheets** for these questions from our website — go to www.cgplearning.co.uk/11+. If you'd prefer to answer them in standard write-in format, just circle the letter underneath your answer. The test should take around 15 minutes.

Section 1 — Complete the Pair

Look at how the first figure is changed, and then work out which option would look like the third figure if you changed it in the same way.

Example:

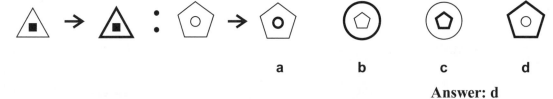

Answer: d

(1)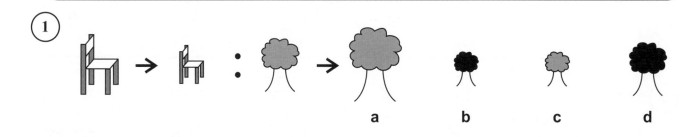

(2)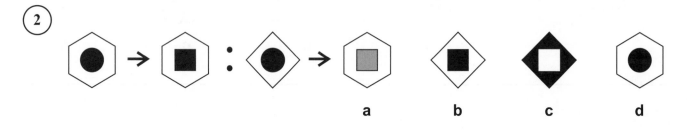

(3)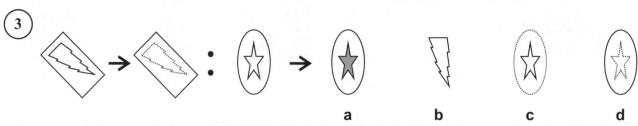

(4)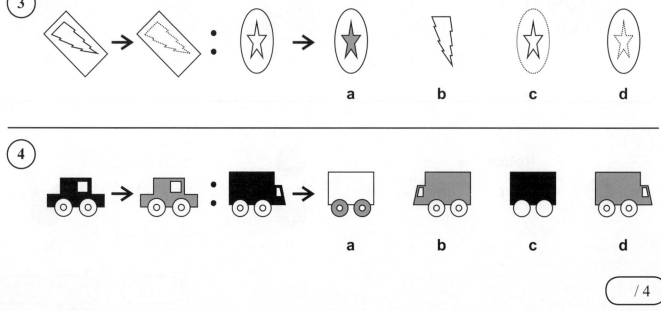

/ 4

Section 2 — Find the Figure Like the First Three

Work out which option is the most like the three figures on the left.

Example:

   |

                                          a   b   c   d

Answer: b

1 |

                                           a   b   c   d

2   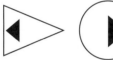  |

                                           a   b   c   d

3 |

                                           a   b   c   d

4    |

                                           a   b   c   d

/ 4

Section 3 — Complete the Grid

Work out which of the options best fits in place of the missing square in the grid.

Example:

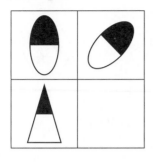

a b c d e

Answer: b

(1)

a b c d e

(2)

a b c d e

(3)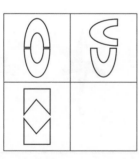

a b c d e

(4)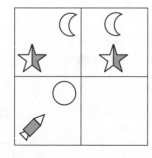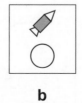

a b c d e

/ 4

Section 4 — Look at the Figure from the Right

Look at the figure on the left. What would it look like if you saw it from the right-hand side? Choose the option on the right which looks like this.

Example:

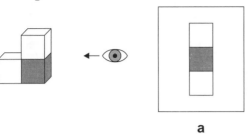 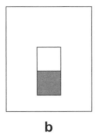 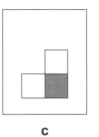 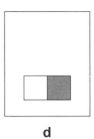

a   b   c   d

Answer: b

---

(1)   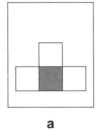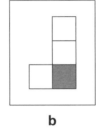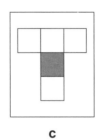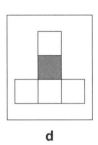

a   b   c   d

---

(2) 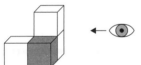   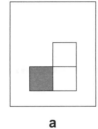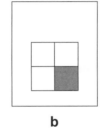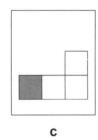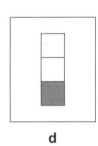

a   b   c   d

---

(3) 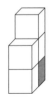   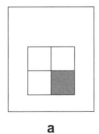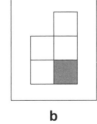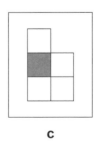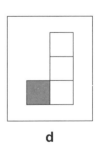

a   b   c   d

---

(4) 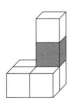   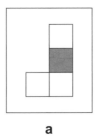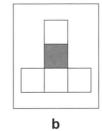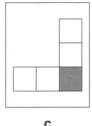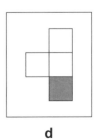

a   b   c   d

/ 4

Assessment Test 4

Section 5 — Complete the Series

Work out which of the options best fits in place of the missing square in the series.

Example:

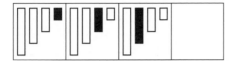

a   b   c   d

Answer: d

1

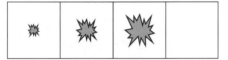

a   b   c   d

2

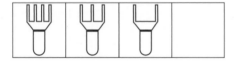

a   b   c   d

3

a   b   c   d

4

a   b   c   d

/ 4

Section 6 — Rotate the Figure

Work out which option would look like the figure on the left if it was rotated.

Example:

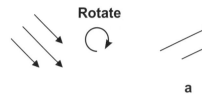

                         a   b   c   d

Answer: b

---

(1)

                         a   b   c   d

---

(2)

                         a   b   c   d

---

(3)

                         a   b   c   d

---

(4)

                         a   b   c   d

/ 4   Total   / 24

Assessment Test 5

You can print **multiple-choice answer sheets** for these questions from our website — go to www.cgplearning.co.uk/11+. If you'd prefer to answer them in standard write-in format, just circle the letter underneath your answer. The test should take around 15 minutes.

Section 1 — Find the Figure Like the First Two

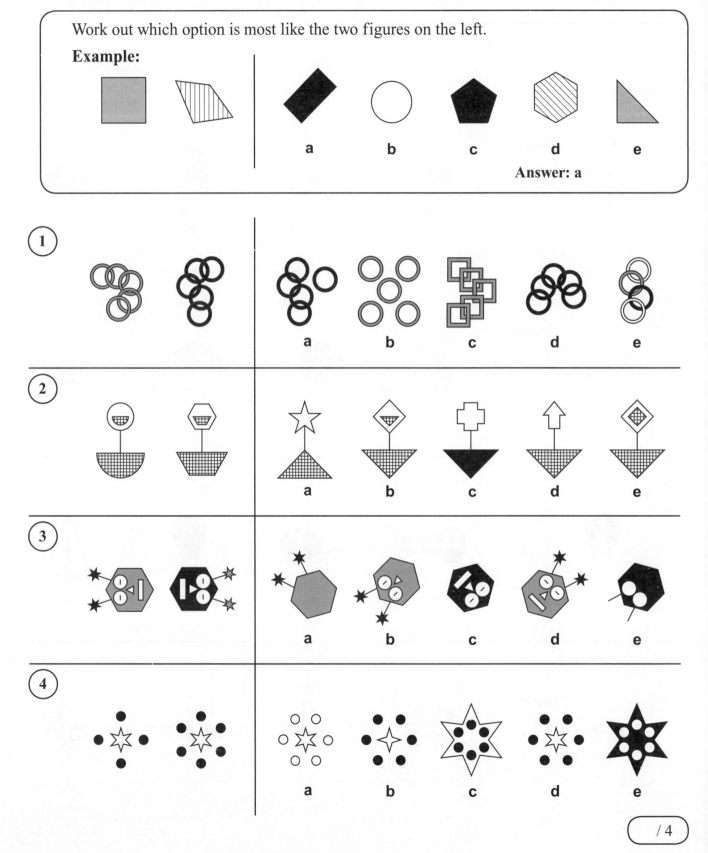

Section 2 — Reflect the Figure

Work out which option would look like the figure on the left if it was reflected over the line.

Example:

Reflect

 |

                                           a   **b**   **c**   **d**

Answer: a

---

(1) Reflect

 |

                                           a   **b**   **c**   **d**

---

(2) Reflect

 |

                                           a   **b**   **c**   **d**

---

(3) Reflect

 |

                                           a   **b**   **c**   **d**

---

(4) Reflect

 |

                                           a   **b**   **c**   **d**

/ 4

Assessment Test 5

Section 3 — Complete the Series

Work out which of the options best fits in place of the missing square in the series.

Example:

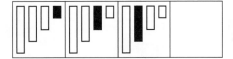

a   b   c   d

Answer: d

(1)

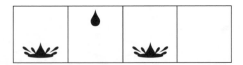

a   b   c   d

(2)

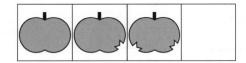

a   b   c   d

(3)

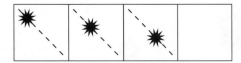

a   b   c   d

(4)

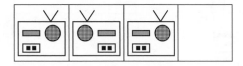

a   b   c   d

/ 4

Section 4 — Look at the Figure from the Right

Look at the figure on the left. What would it look like if you saw it from the right-hand side? Choose the option on the right which looks like this.

Example:

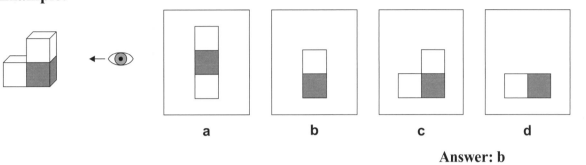

a   b   c   d

Answer: b

1

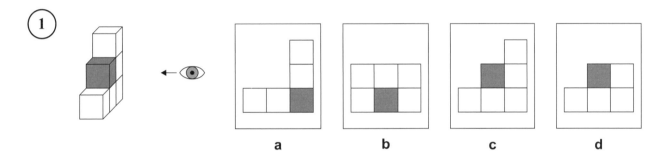

a   b   c   d

2

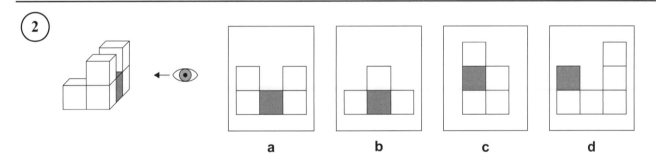

a   b   c   d

3

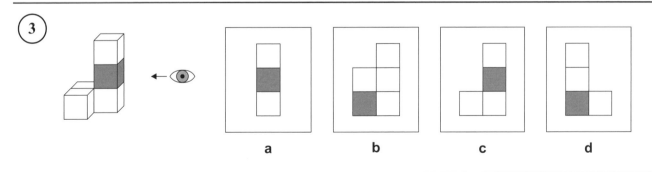

a   b   c   d

4

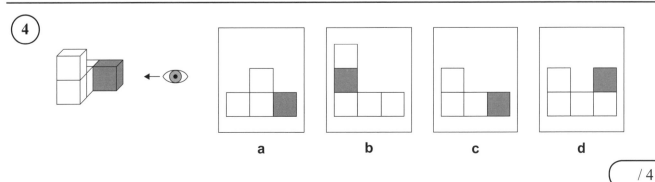

a   b   c   d

/ 4

Section 5 — Rotate the Figure

Work out which option would look like the figure on the left if it was rotated.

Example:

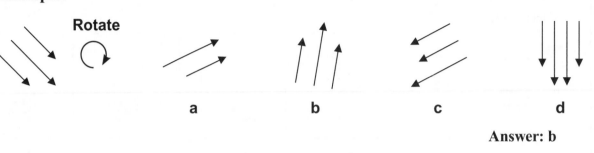

a   b   c   d

Answer: b

---

(1) **Rotate**

a   b   c   d

---

(2) **Rotate**

a   b   c   d

---

(3) **Rotate**

a   b   c   d

---

(4) **Rotate**

a   b   c   d

/ 4

Section 6 — Complete the Grid

Work out which of the options best fits in place of the missing square in the grid.

Example:

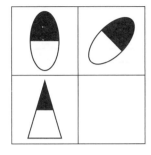

a

b

c

d

Answer: b

(1)

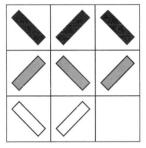

a   **b**   **c**   **d**

(2)

a   **b**   **c**   **d**

(3)

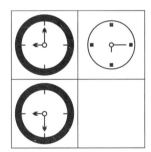

a   **b**   **c**   **d**

(4)

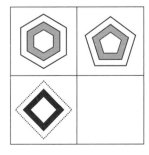

a   **b**   **c**   **d**

/ 4   Total   / 24

END OF TEST

Assessment Test 5

Assessment Test 6

You can print **multiple-choice answer sheets** for these questions from our website — go to www.cgplearning.co.uk/11+. If you'd prefer to answer them in standard write-in format, just circle the letter underneath your answer. The test should take around 15 minutes.

Section 1 — Rotate the Figure

Work out which option would look like the figure on the left if it was rotated.

Example:

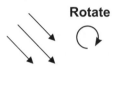

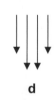

a   b   c   d

Answer: b

① Rotate

a   b   c   d

② 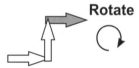 Rotate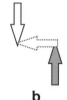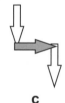

a   b   c   d

③ Rotate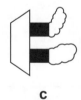

a   b   c   d

④ Rotate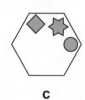

a   b   c   d

/ 4

Section 2 — Complete the Pair

Look at how the first figure is changed, and then work out which option would look like the third figure if you changed it in the same way.

Example:

a b c d e

Answer: d

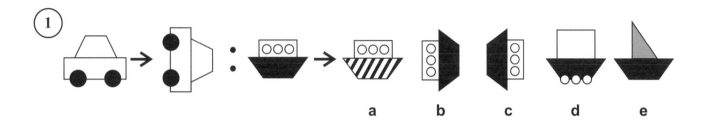

1

a b c d e

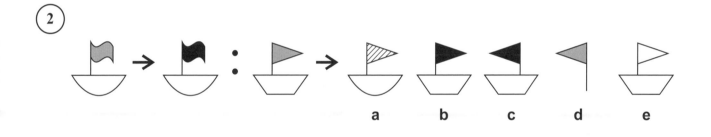

2

a b c d e

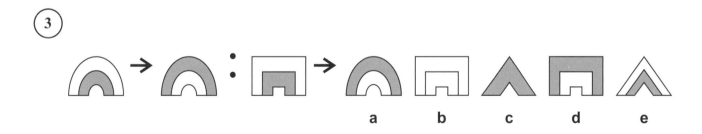

3

a b c d e

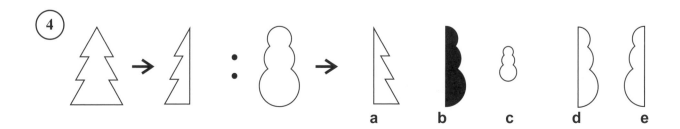

4

a b c d e

/4

Assessment Test 6

Section 3 — Look at the Figure from the Top

Look at the figure on the left. What would it look like if you saw it from the top?
Choose the option on the right which looks like this.

Example:

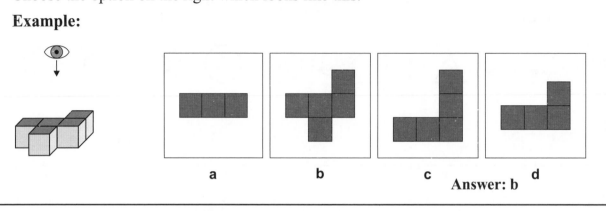

a   b   c   d

Answer: b

1

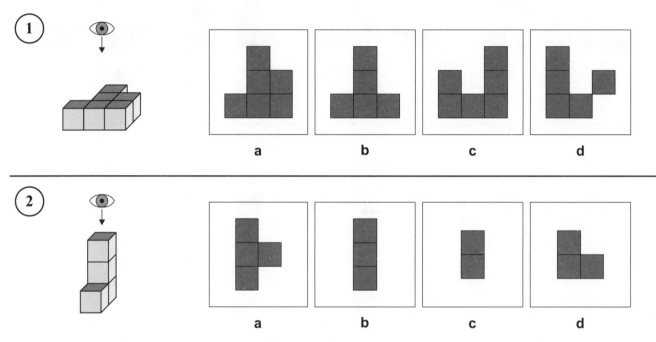

a   b   c   d

2

a   b   c   d

3

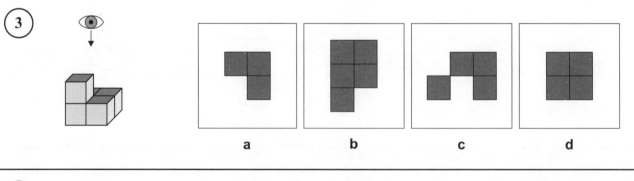

a   b   c   d

4

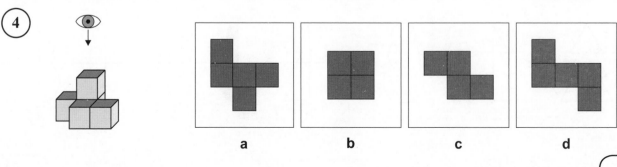

a   b   c   d

/ 4

Section 4 — Reflect the Figure

Work out which option would look like the figure on the left if it was reflected over the line.

Example:

Reflect

a   b   c   d

Answer: a

(1) **Reflect**

a   b   c   d

(2) **Reflect**

a   b   c   d

(3) **Reflect**

a   b   c   d

(4) **Reflect**

a   b   c   d

/ 4

Assessment Test 6

Section 5 — Odd One Out

Find the figure in each row that is most unlike the other figures.

Example:

a   b   c   d   e

Answer: a

1

a   b   c   d   e

2

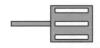

a   b   c   d   e

3

a   b   c   d   e

4

a   b   c   d   e

/ 4

Section 6 — Find the Figure Like the First Three

Work out which option is the most like the three figures on the left.

Example:

a   b   c   d

Answer: b

 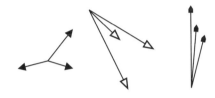

a   b   c   d

a   b   c   d

a   b   c   d

a   b   c   d

/ 4   Total   / 24

END OF TEST

Assessment Test 6

Assessment Test 7

You can print **multiple-choice answer sheets** for these questions from our website — go to www.cgplearning.co.uk/11+. If you'd prefer to answer them in standard write-in format, just circle the letter underneath your answer. The test should take around 15 minutes.

Section 1 — Complete the Series

Work out which of the options best fits in place of the missing square in the series.

Example:

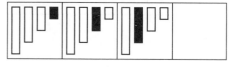

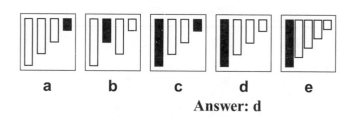

a   b   c   d   e

Answer: d

(1)

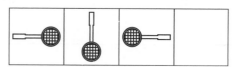

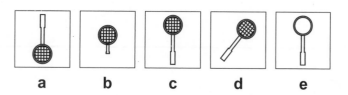

a   b   c   d   e

(2)

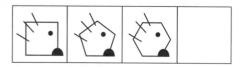

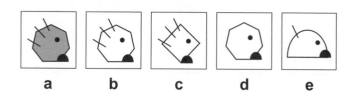

a   b   c   d   e

(3)

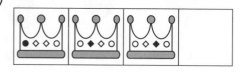

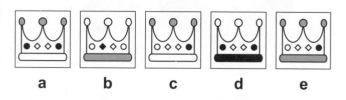

a   b   c   d   e

(4)

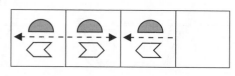

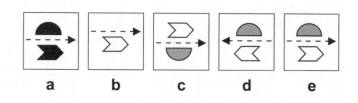

a   b   c   d   e

/ 4

Section 2 — Find the Figure Like the First Two

Work out which option is most like the two figures on the left.

Example:

a   b   c   d

Answer: a

1

a   b   c   d

2

a   b   c   d

3

a   b   c   d

4

a   b   c   d

/ 4

Assessment Test 7

Section 3 — Rotate the Figure

Work out which option would look like the figure on the left if it was rotated.

Example:

Rotate

a

b

c

d

Answer: b

(1) Rotate

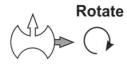

a

b

c

d

(2) Rotate

a

b

c

d

(3) Rotate

a

b

c

d

(4) Rotate

a

b

c

d

/ 4

Assessment Test 7

Section 4 — Complete the Pair

Look at how the first two figures are changed, and then work out which option would look like the third figure if you changed it in the same way.

Example:

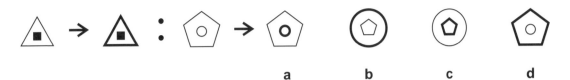

Answer: d

1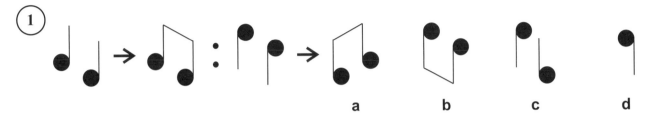

2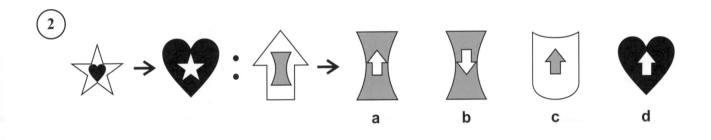

3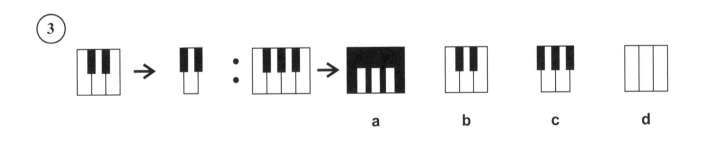

4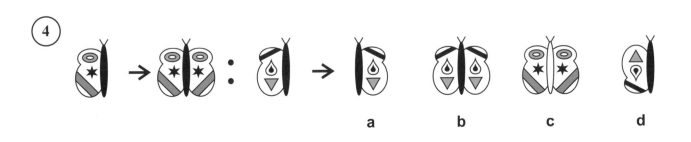

60

Section 5 — Look at the Figure from the Right

Look at the figure on the left. What would it look like if you saw it from the right-hand side? Choose the option on the right which looks like this.

Example:

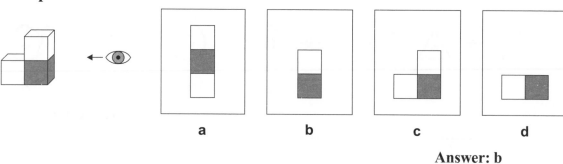

Answer: **b**

1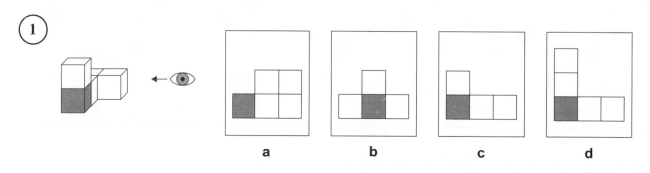

2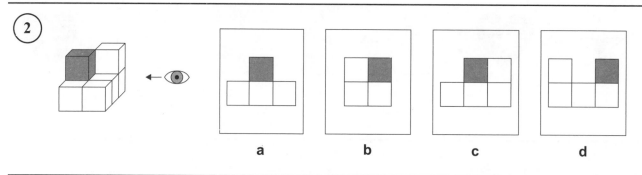

3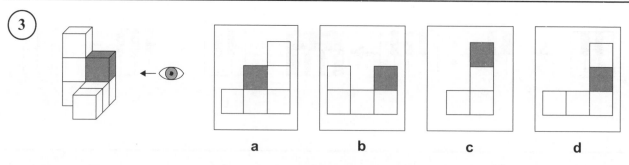

4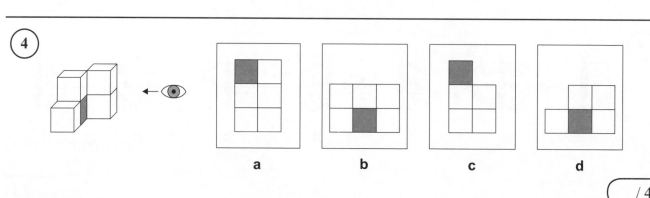

/ 4

Assessment Test 7

Section 6 — Complete the Grid

Work out which of the options best fits in place of the missing square in the grid.

Example:

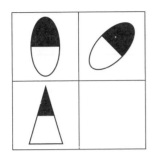

a   b   c   d   e

Answer: b

 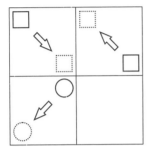

a   b   c   d   e

a   b   c   d   e

 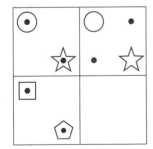

a   b   c   d   e

a   b   c   d   e

 / 4   Total / 24

END OF TEST

Assessment Test 7

Assessment Test 8

You can print **multiple-choice answer sheets** for these questions from our website — go to www.cgplearning.co.uk/11+. If you'd prefer to answer them in standard write-in format, just circle the letter underneath your answer. The test should take around 15 minutes.

Section 1 — Complete the Pair

Look at how the first figure is changed, and then work out which option would look like the third figure if you changed it in the same way.

Example:

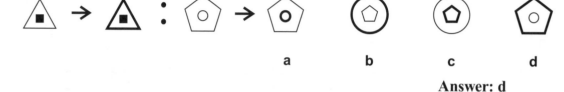

Answer: d

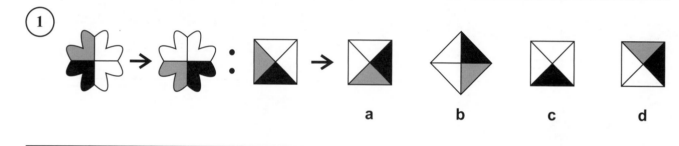

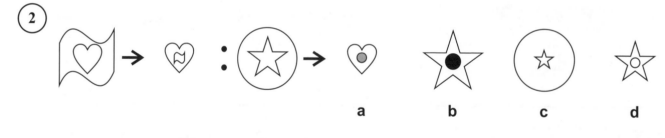

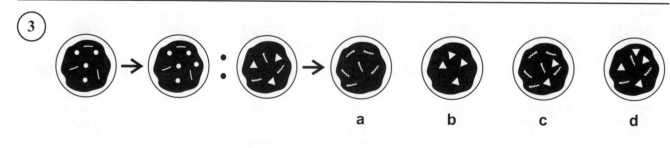

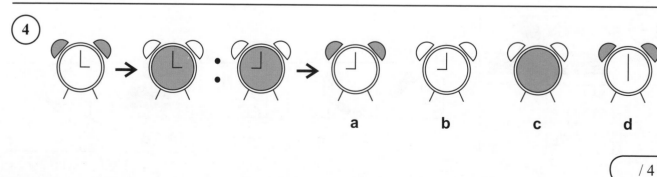

/4

Section 2 — Look at the Figure from the Top

Look at the figure on the left. What would it look like if you saw it from the top? Choose the option on the right which looks like this.

Example:

 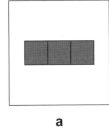 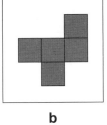  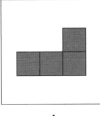

a   b   c   **Answer: b**   d

1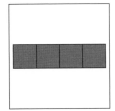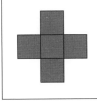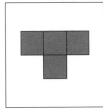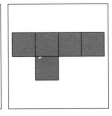

a   b   c   d

2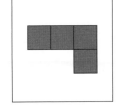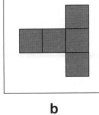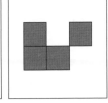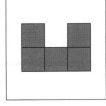

a   b   c   d

3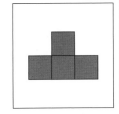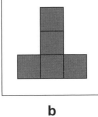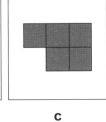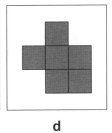

a   b   c   d

4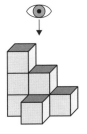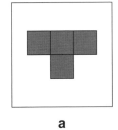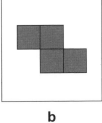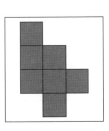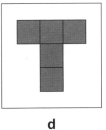

a   b   c   d

/ 4

Assessment Test 8

Section 3 — Complete the Series

Work out which of the options best fits in place of the missing square in the series.

Example:

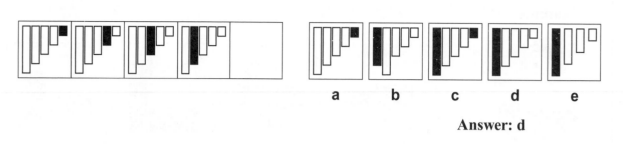

Answer: d

1

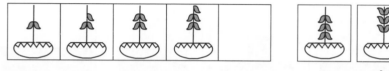 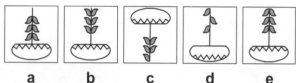

2

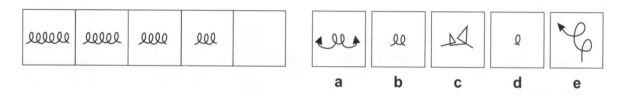

3

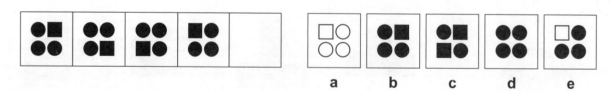

4

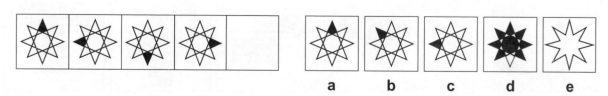

/ 4

Section 4 — Reflect the Figure

Work out which option would look like the figure on the left if it was reflected over the line.

Example:

Reflect

a   b   c   d

Answer: a

1 Reflect

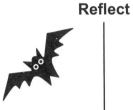

a   b   c   d

2 Reflect

a   b   c   d

3 Reflect

a   b   c   d

4 Reflect

a   b   c   d

/ 4

Assessment Test 8

Section 5 — Find the Figure Like the First Three

Work out which option is the most like the three figures on the left.

Example:

a b c d

Answer: b

(1)

a b c d

(2)

a b c d

(3)

a b c d

(4)

a b c d

/ 4

Assessment Test 8

Section 6 — Odd One Out

Find the figure in each row that is most unlike the other figures.

Example:

a   b   c   d   e

Answer: a

(1)

a   b   c   d   e

(2)

a   b   c   d   e

(3)

a   b   c   d   e

(4)

a   b   c   d   e

/ 4   Total / 24

END OF TEST   *Assessment Test 8*

Assessment Test 9

You can print **multiple-choice answer sheets** for these questions from our website — go to www.cgplearning.co.uk/11+. If you'd prefer to answer them in standard write-in format, just circle the letter underneath your answer. The test should take around 15 minutes.

Section 1 — Find the Figure Like the First Two

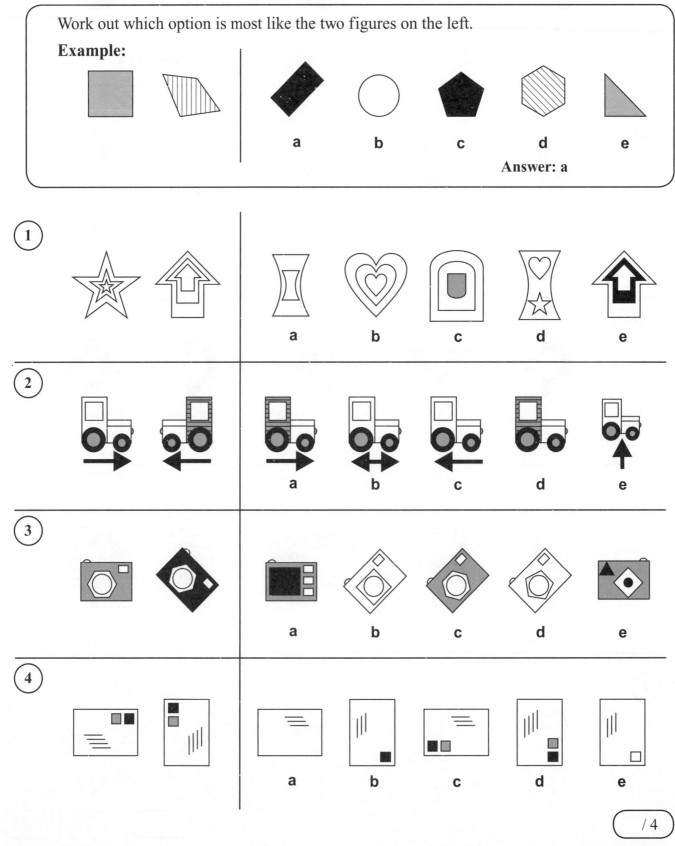

/ 4

Section 2 — Complete the Grid

Work out which of the options best fits in place of the missing square in the grid.

Example:

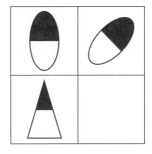

a   b   c   d

Answer: b

① 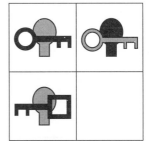

a   b   c   d

② 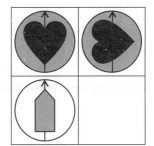

a   b   c   d

③ 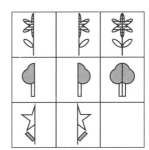

a   b   c   d

④ 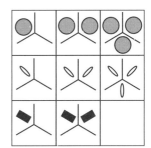

a   b   c   d

/ 4

Section 3 — Complete the Series

Work out which of the options best fits in place of the missing square in the series.

Example:

a   b   c   d

Answer: d

1

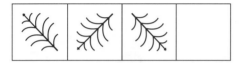

a   b   c   d

2

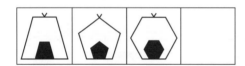

a   b   c   d

3

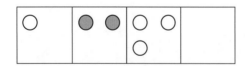

a   b   c   d

4

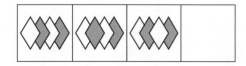

a   b   c   d

/ 4

Section 4 — Reflect the Figure

Work out which option would look like the figure on the left if it was reflected over the line.

Example:

Reflect

         a   b   c   d

Answer: a

---

(1)   **Reflect**

         a   b   c   d

---

(2)   **Reflect**

  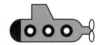

         a   b   c   d

---

(3)   **Reflect**

         a   b   c   d

---

(4)   **Reflect**

         a   b   c   d

/ 4

72

Section 5 — Odd One Out

Find the figure in each row that is most unlike the other figures.

Example:

a   b   c   d   e

Answer: a

(1)

a   b   c   d   e

(2)

a   b   c   d   e

(3)

a   b   c   d   e

(4)

a   b   c   d   e

/ 4

Assessment Test 9

Section 6 — Complete the Pair

Look at how the first figure is changed, and then work out which option would look like the third figure if you changed it in the same way.

Example:

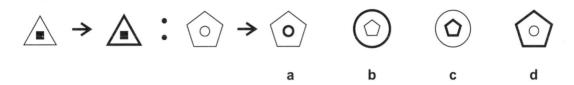

a   b   c   d

Answer: d

1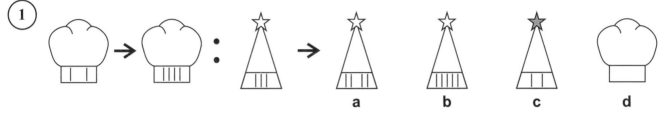

a   b   c   d

2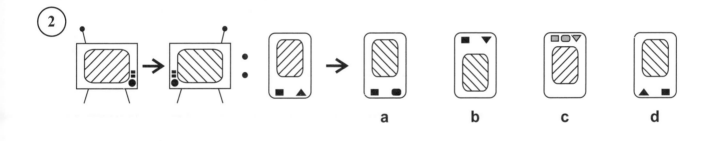

a   b   c   d

3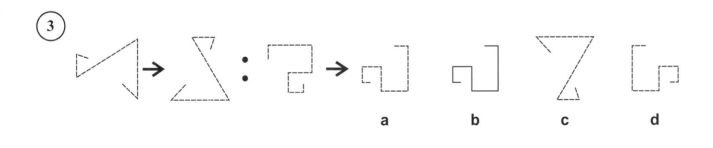

a   b   c   d

4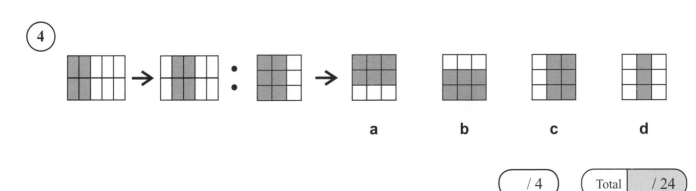

a   b   c   d

/ 4   Total / 24

END OF TEST   *Assessment Test 9*

Assessment Test 10

You can print **multiple-choice answer sheets** for these questions from our website — go to www.cgplearning.co.uk/11+. If you'd prefer to answer them in standard write-in format, just circle the letter underneath your answer. The test should take around 15 minutes.

Section 1 — Find the Figure Like the First Three

Work out which option is the most like the three figures on the left.

Example:

   |

a   b   c   d

Answer: b

(1) |

a   b   c   d

(2) |

a   b   c   d

(3) |

a   b   c   d

(4)  |

a   b   c   d

/ 4

Section 2 — Rotate the Figure

Work out which option would look like the figure on the left if it was rotated.

Example:

 Rotate

a

b

c

d

Answer: b

1 **Rotate**

a

b

c

d

2 **Rotate**

a

b

c

d

3 **Rotate**

a

b

c

d

4 **Rotate**

a

b

c

d

/ 4

Assessment Test 10

Section 3 – Reflect the Figure

Work out which option would look like the figure on the left if it was reflected over the line.

Example:

Reflect

a b c d

Answer: a

---

(1) **Reflect**

a b c d

---

(2) **Reflect**

a b c d

---

(3) **Reflect**

a b c d

---

(4) **Reflect**

a b c d

/ 4

Assessment Test 10

Section 4 — Complete the Series

Work out which of the options best fits in place of the missing square in the series.

Example:

                   a   **b**   **c**   **d**

Answer: d

1

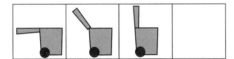

                   a   **b**   **c**   **d**

2

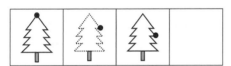

                   a   **b**   **c**   **d**

3

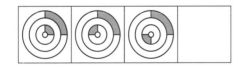

                   a   **b**   **c**   **d**

4

                   a   **b**   **c**   **d**

/ 4

Section 5 — Complete the Pair

Look at how the first figure is changed, and then work out which option would look like the third figure if you changed it in the same way.

Example:

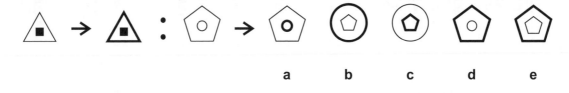

a   b   c   d   e

Answer: d

(1)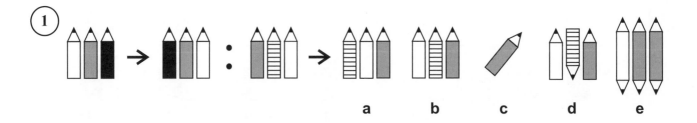

a   b   c   d   e

(2)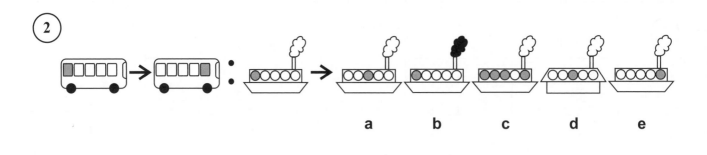

a   b   c   d   e

(3)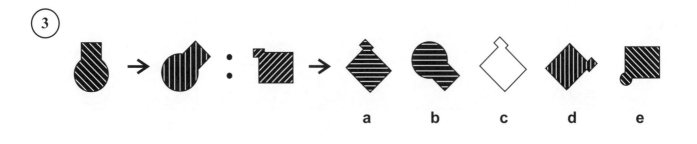

a   b   c   d   e

(4)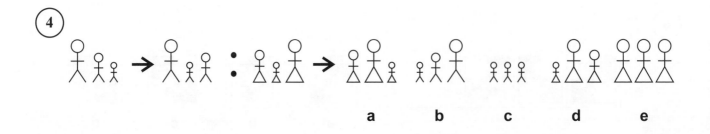

a   b   c   d   e

/ 4

Section 6 — Look at the Figure from the Top

Look at the figure on the left. What would it look like if you saw it from the top? Choose the option on the right which looks like this.

Example:

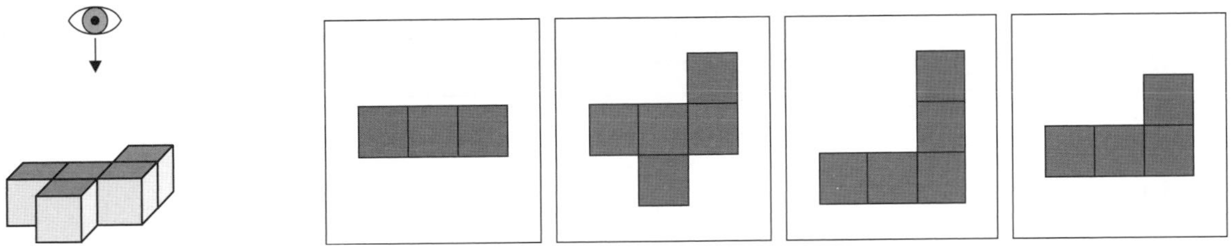

a   b   c   d

Answer: b

1

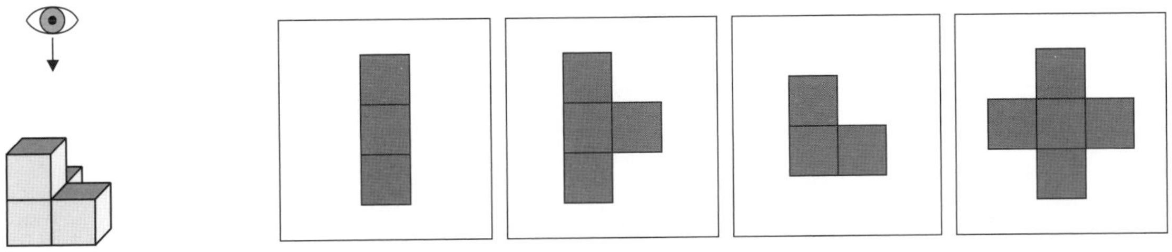

a   b   c   d

2

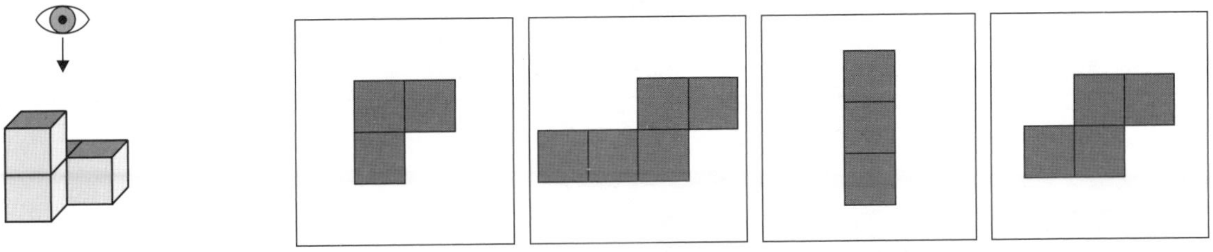

a   b   c   d

3

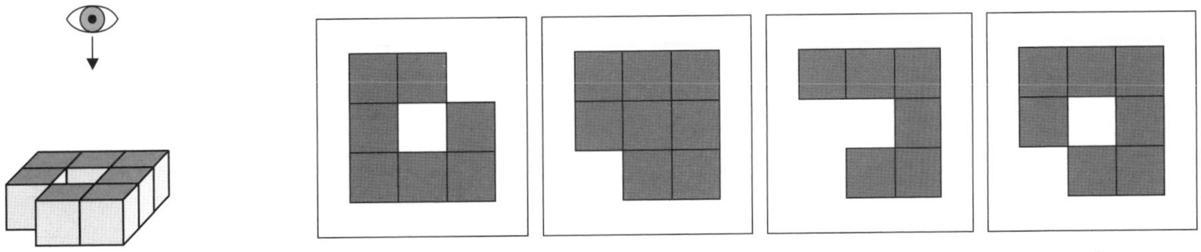

a   b   c   d

4

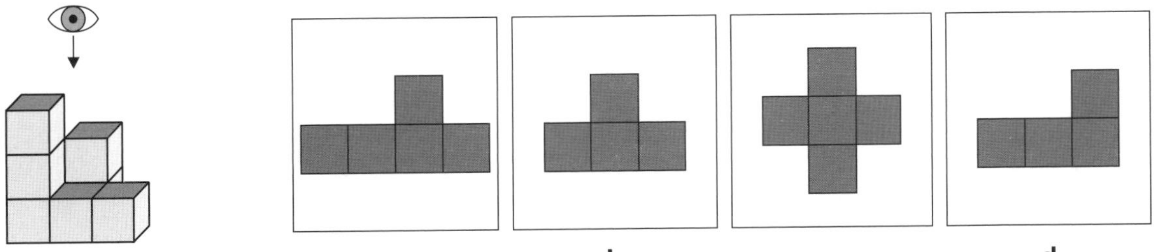

a   b   c   d

/ 4   Total   / 24

END OF TEST

Assessment Test 10

Assessment Test 11

You can print **multiple-choice answer sheets** for these questions from our website — go to www.cgplearning.co.uk/11+. If you'd prefer to answer them in standard write-in format, just circle the letter underneath your answer. The test should take around 15 minutes.

Section 1 — Find the Figure Like the First Two

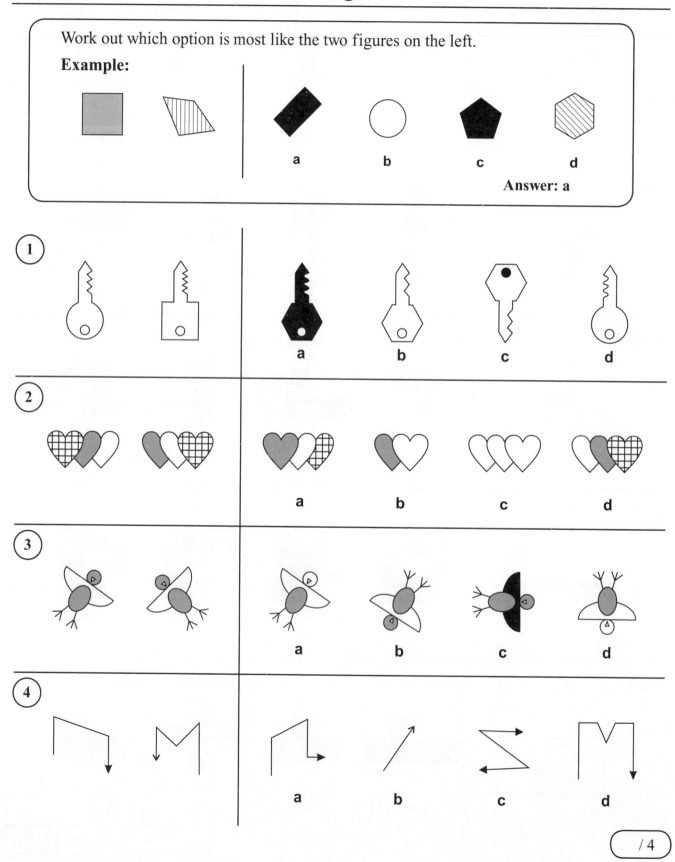

/ 4

Section 2 — Odd One Out

Find the figure in each row that is most unlike the other figures.

Example:

a   b   c   d   e

Answer: a

---

(1)

a   b   c   d   e

---

(2)

a   b   c   d   e

---

(3)

a   b   c   d   e

---

(4)

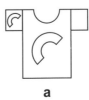
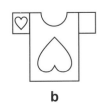
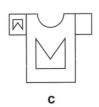
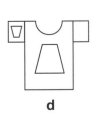
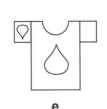

a   b   c   d   e

/ 4

Assessment Test 11

Section 3 — Reflect the Figure

Work out which option would look like the figure on the left if it was reflected over the line.

Example:

Reflect

a   b   c   d

Answer: a

---

(1)   **Reflect**

   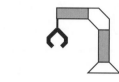

a   b   c   d

---

(2)   **Reflect**

a   b   c   d

---

(3)   **Reflect**

a   b   c   d

---

(4)   **Reflect**

a   b   c   d

/ 4

Section 4 — Look at the Figure from the Right

Look at the figure on the left. What would it look like if you saw it from the right-hand side? Choose the option on the right which looks like this.

Example:

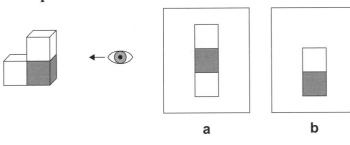 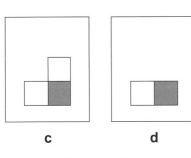

a   b   c   d

Answer: b

1

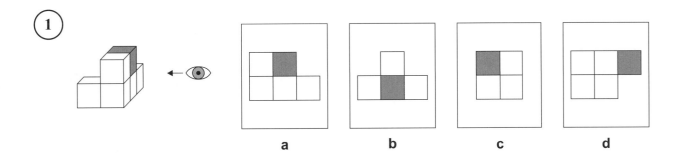

a   b   c   d

2

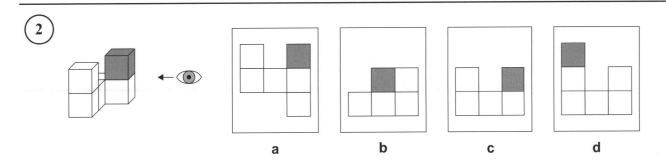

a   b   c   d

3

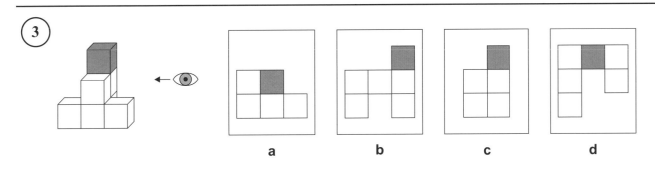

a   b   c   d

4

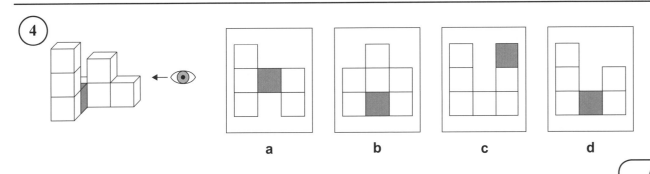

a   b   c   d

/ 4

Section 5 — Complete the Grid

Work out which of the options best fits in place of the missing square in the grid.

Example:

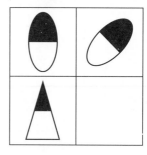

                           a   b   c   d   e

Answer: b

(1)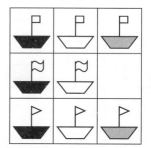

                           a   b   c   d   e

(2)

                           a   b   c   d   e

(3)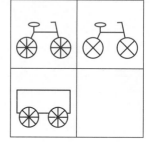

                           a   b   c   d   e

(4)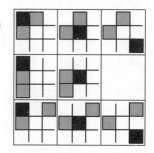

                           a   b   c   d   e

/ 4

Section 6 — Rotate the Figure

Work out which option would look like the figure on the left if it was rotated.

Example:

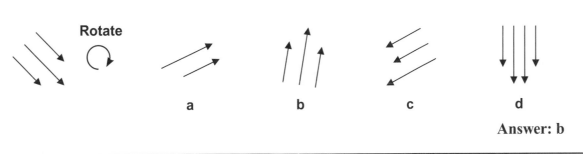

Answer: b

a   b   c   d

a   b   c   d

a   b   c   d

a   b   c   d

/ 4   Total   / 24

END OF TEST

Assessment Test 11

Glossary

Rotation

Rotation is when a shape is **turned** clockwise or anticlockwise.

Example shape

45 degree rotation

90 degree rotation

180 degree rotation

Clockwise is the direction that the hands on a clock move

Anticlockwise is the opposite direction

Reflection

Reflection is when something is **mirrored** over a line (this line might be invisible).

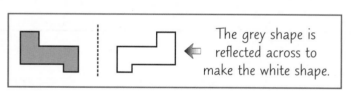
The grey shape is reflected across to make the white shape.

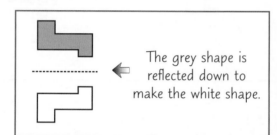
The grey shape is reflected down to make the white shape.

Other terms

Figure — the picture as a whole that makes up one example or option in a question.

Line Types:

 Thin
 Thick
 Dashed
 Dotted
 Curved
 Jagged
Wavy

Shading Types:

 Black
Grey
 White
  Two types of hatching
 Cross-hatched
 Spotted

Layering — when a shape is in front of or behind another shape, or when shapes overlap each other.

The circle is in front of the square.

Symmetry — a shape is symmetrical if it can be split into halves that are reflections of each other.